Dear Parents,

Welcome to the Scholastic Reader series. We have taken over 80 years of experience with teachers, parents, and children and put it into a program that is designed to match your child's interests and skills.

Level 1—Short sentences and stories made up of words kids can sound out using their phonics skills and words that are important to remember.

Level 2—Longer sentences and stories with words kids need to know and new "big" words that they will want to know.

Level 3—From sentences to paragraphs to longer stories, these books have large "chunks" of texts and are made up of a rich vocabulary.

Level 4—First chapter books with more words and fewer pictures.

It is important that children learn to read well enough to succeed in school and beyond. Here are ideas for reading this book with your child:

- Look at the book together. Encourage your child to read the title and make a prediction about the story.
- Read the book together. Encourage your child to sound out words when appropriate. When your child struggles, you can help by providing the word.
- Encourage your child to retell the story. This is a great way to check for comprehension.
- Have your child take the fluency test on the last page to check progress.

Scholastic Readers are designed to support your child's efforts to learn how to read at every age and every stage. Enjoy helping your child learn to read and love to read.

—Francie Alexander
Chief Education Officer
Scholastic Education

Copyright © 1994 by Nancy Hall, Inc.
Fluency activities copyright © 2003 Scholastic Inc.
All rights reserved. Published by Scholastic Inc.
SCHOLASTIC, CARTWHEEL BOOKS, and associated logos
are trademarks and/or registered trademarks of Scholastic Inc.

Library of Congress Cataloging-in-Publication Data is available.

ISBN: 0-439-62593-9

10 9 8 7 6 5 4 3 2 1   07
Printed in the U.S.A. 23 • First printing, October 1994

The Pet That I Want

by **Mary Packard**

Illustrated by **John Magine**

Scholastic Reader — Level 1

SCHOLASTIC INC.

New York   Toronto   London   Auckland   Sydney
Mexico City   New Delhi   Hong Kong   Buenos Aires

The pet that I want

does not have fur.

It does not like to cuddle.

It does not like to purr.

The pet that I want

does not go tweet,

or carry a shell,

or have funny feet.

The pet that I want

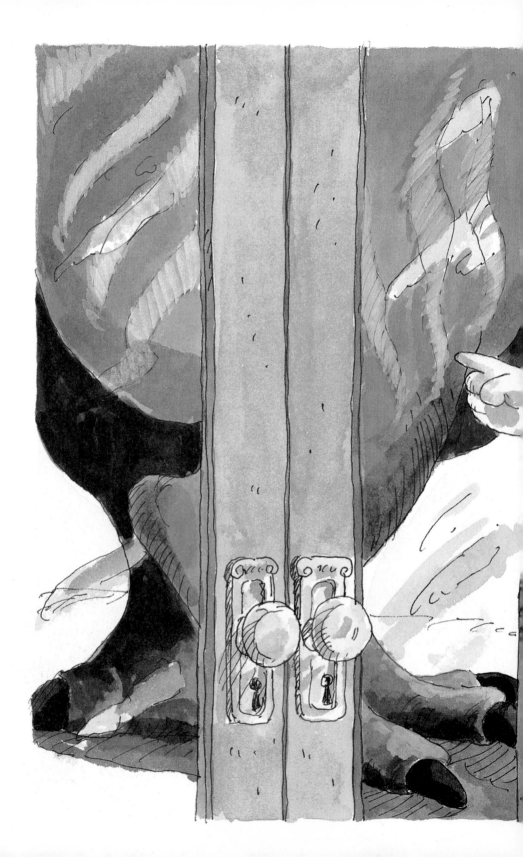

does not fit through the door.

The pet that I want is a
dinosaur!

The Pet That She Wants

The girl does not want a pet with feathers.

She does not want a pet with stripes.

She does not want a pet with a long neck.

She does not want a pet with fins.

Which of these pictures might be the pet that she wants?

Which Pet Did What?

Go back to the story.

Which pet likes to cuddle?

Which likes to purr?

Which goes tweet?

Which has a shell?

Pet Fun

Here are some pets doing many things. Which ones could be real? Point to them. Now point to the ones that are make-believe.

Time to Rhyme

Words that rhyme sound alike. Point to the picture that rhymes with the word at the beginning of each row.

shell

my

funny

like

The Pet for You

If you could choose one of these pets, which would it be?

Why did you choose that one?

Picking a Home for a Pet

Match each pet with its home.

Answers

(The Pet That She Wants)

(Which Pet Did What?)

cuddle   purr   tweet   shell

(Pet Fun)

real:

make-believe:

(Time to Rhyme)

shell   my   funny   like

(The Pet for You)   Answers will vary.

(Picking a Home for a Pet)